piano • vocal • guitar

olivia rodrigo
GUTS

ISBN 979-835011025-8

Visit Hal Leonard Online at
www.halleonard.com

World headquarters, contact:
Hal Leonard
7777 West Bluemound Road
Milwaukee, WI 53213
Email: info@halleonard.com

In Europe, contact:
Hal Leonard Europe Limited
1 Red Place
London, W1K 6PL
Email: info@halleonardeurope.com

In Australia, contact:
Hal Leonard Australia Pty. Ltd.
4 Lentara Court
Cheltenham, Victoria, 3192 Australia
Email: info@halleonard.com.au

ALL-AMERICAN BITCH

Words and Music by OLIVIA RODRIGO
and DANIEL NIGRO

Recorded a half step lower.

BAD IDEA RIGHT?

Words and Music by OLIVIA RODRIGO
and DANIEL NIGRO

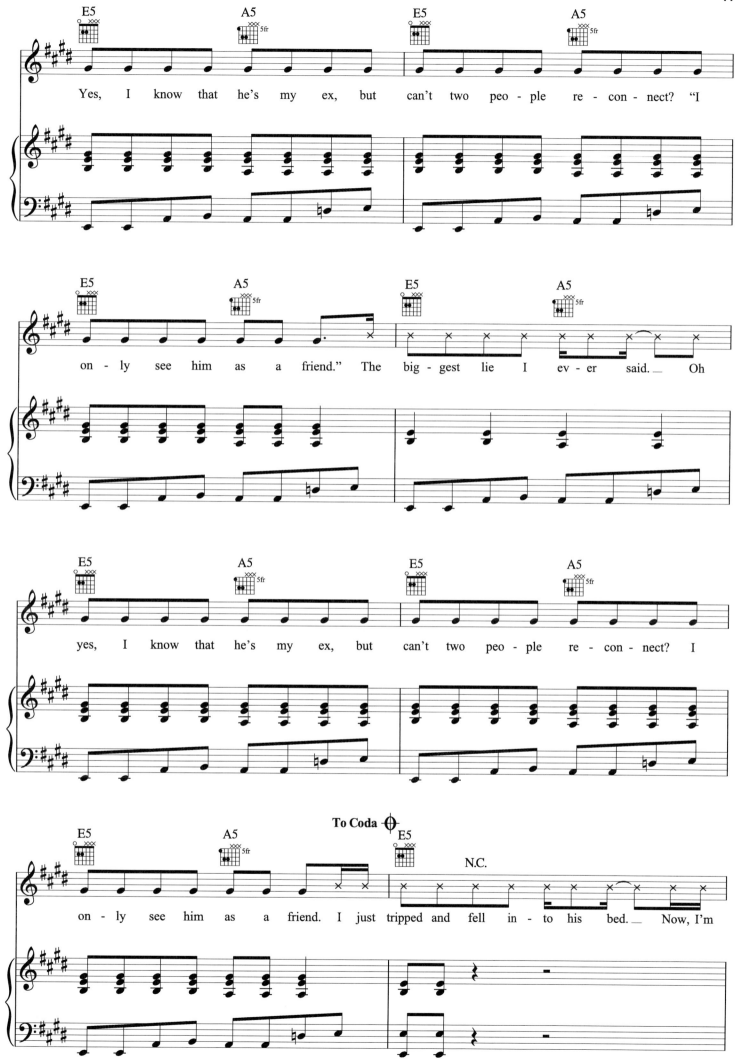

VAMPIRE

Words and Music by OLIVIA RODRIGO
and DANIEL NIGRO

LACY

Words and Music by OLIVIA RODRIGO
and DANIEL NIGRO

BALLAD OF A HOMESCHOOLED GIRL

Words and Music by OLIVIA RODRIGO
and DANIEL NIGRO

The morn-ing af-ter I pan - ic: "Oh God, what did I say?"

Wan-na curl up and die.___ It's so-cial su-i-cide.__ Yeah,__

___ when I'm a-lone I'm fine,__ but don't let me out at night.__

It's so-cial su-i-cide.__ It's so-cial su-i-cide.__ Ah,___

MAKING THE BED

Words and Music by OLIVIA RODRIGO
and DANIEL NIGRO

Moody Ballad, in 2

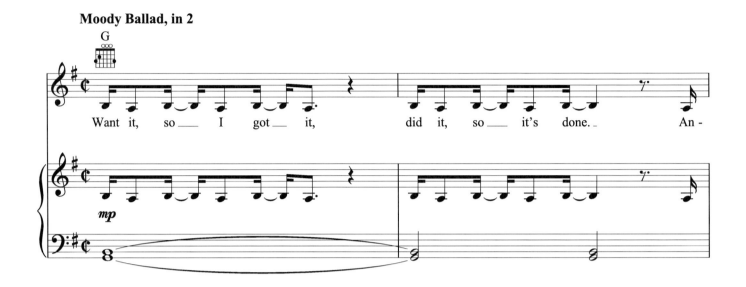

Want it, so __ I got __ it, did it, so __ it's done. __ An-

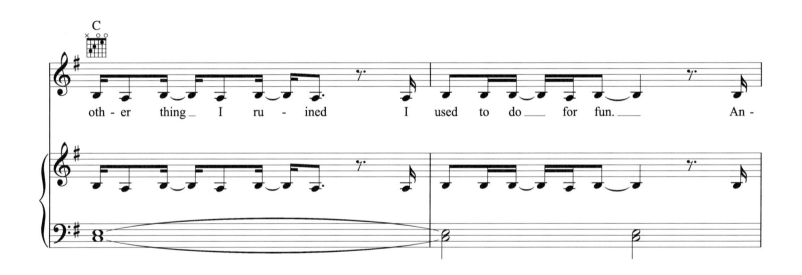

oth-er thing __ I ru-ined I used to do __ for fun. __ An-

oth-er piece __ of plas-tic I could just throw a-way, __ an-

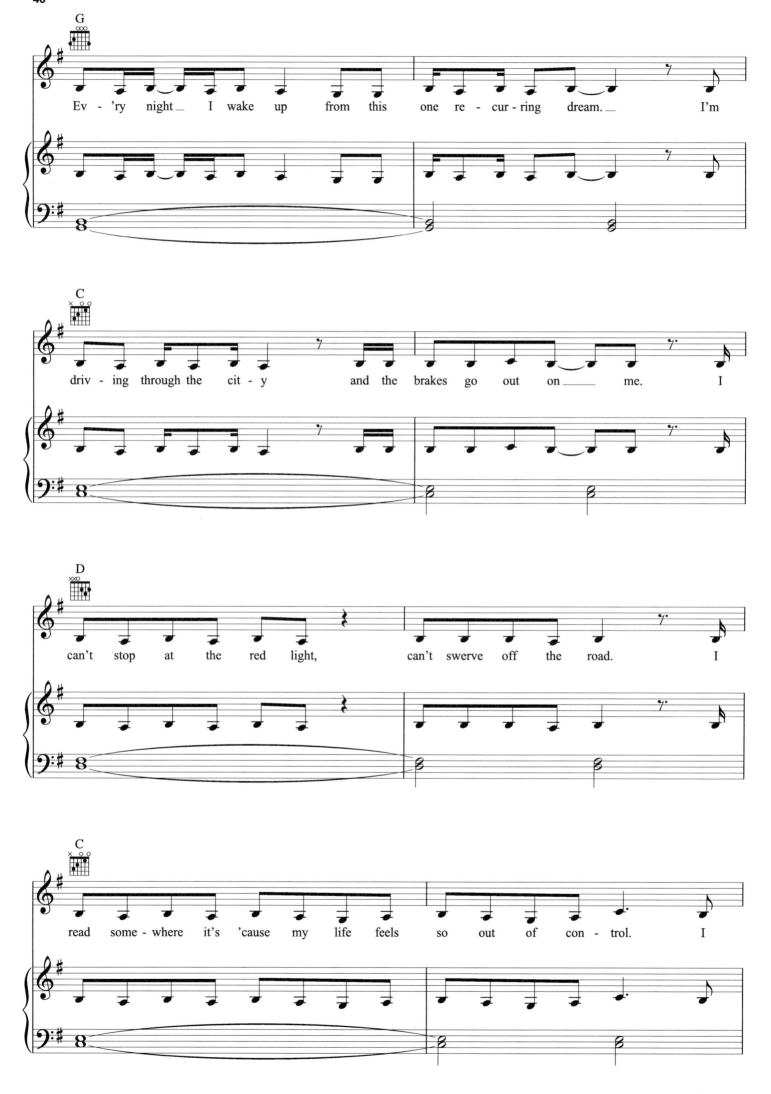

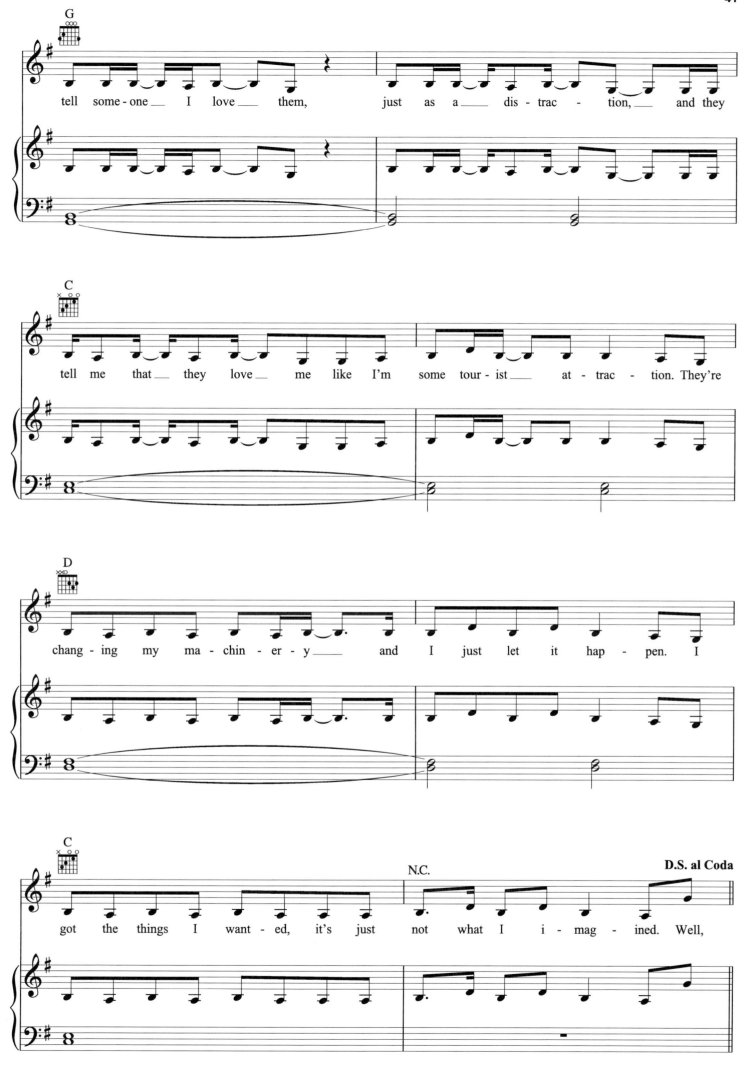

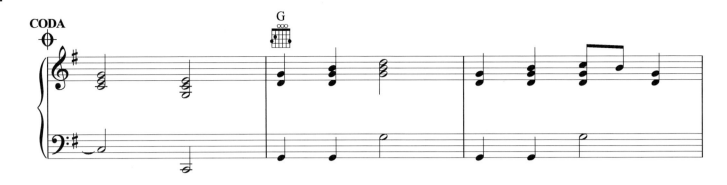

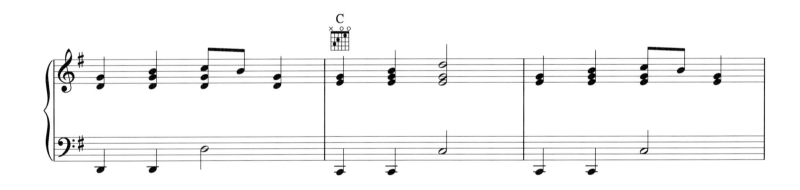

Some-times I feel___ like I don't___ wan-na be___ where I am.___

LOGICAL

Words and Music by OLIVIA RODRIGO,
DANIEL NIGRO and JULIA MICHAELS

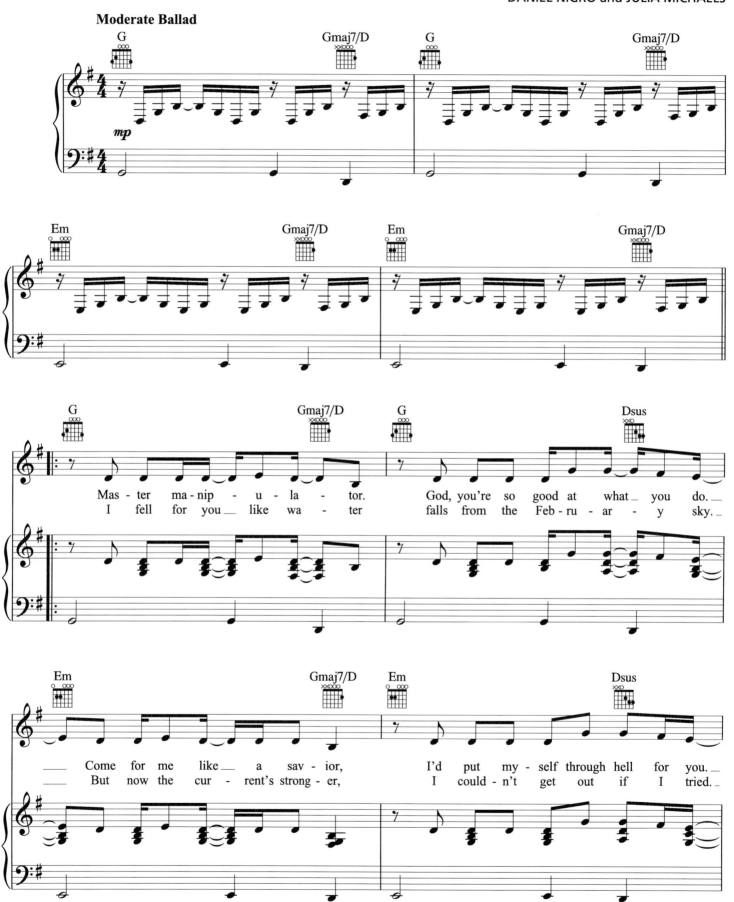

Master manipulator. God, you're so good at what you do.

I fell for you like water falls from the February sky.

Come for me like a savior, I'd put myself through hell for you.

But now the current's stronger, I couldn't get out if I tried.

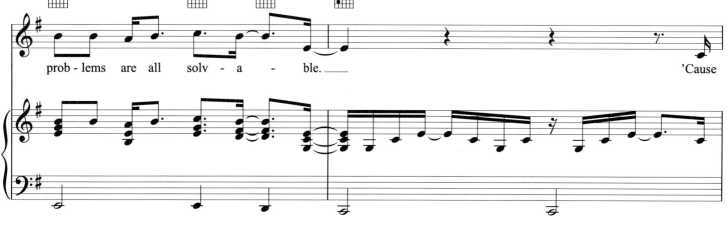

Em   **C/E**   **Gmaj7/D**   **C**

chang - ing you is pos - si - ble. ___   I guess

Cmaj7/D   **G**   **Dsus**

love is nev - er log - i - cal. The sky is green, the grass __ is red, __ and

G   **Dsus**   **Em**   **Em/D**

you mean all those words __ you said. __ I'm sure that girl is real - ly your friend. Our

Em   **C/E**   **Gmaj7/D**   **C**

prob - lems are all solv - a - ble. ___   'Cause

love is nev - er log - i - cal. __ I know I'm half __ re - spon - si - ble and

that makes me __ feel hor - ri - ble. __ Oh, log - i - cal, log - i - cal,

love is nev - er log - i - cal. __ I could have gone __ and stopped it all. __ God,

why did - n't __ I stop __ it all? Oh, why did - n't __ I stop __ it all? __

GET HIM BACK!

Words and Music by OLIVIA RODRIGO
and DANIEL NIGRO

Additional Lyrics

Rap I: I met a guy in the summer and I left him in the spring.
He argued with me about everything.
He had an ego and a temper and a wandering eye.
He said he's six foot two, and I'm like, "Dude, nice try."

But he was so much fun, and he had such weird friends.
And he would take us out to parties and the night would never end.
Another song, another club, another bar, another dance,
And when he said something wrong, he'd just fly me to France.

So I miss him some nights when I'm feeling depressed,
Till I remember every time he made a pass on my friend.
Do I love him, do I hate him? I guess it's up and down.
If I had to choose, I would say right now...

Rap II: So I write him all these letters and I throw them in the trash
Cuz I miss the way he kisses and the way he made me laugh.
Yeah, I pour my little heart out, but as I'm hitting send
I picture all the faces of my disappointed friends.

Because everyone knew all of the shit that he'd do.
He said I was the only girl, but that just wasn't the truth.
And when I told him how he hurt me, he'd tell me I was tripping.
But I am my father's daughter, so maybe I could fix him!

LOVE IS EMBARRASSING

Words and Music by OLIVIA RODRIGO
and DANIEL NIGRO

THE GRUDGE

Words and Music by OLIVIA RODRIGO
and DANIEL NIGRO

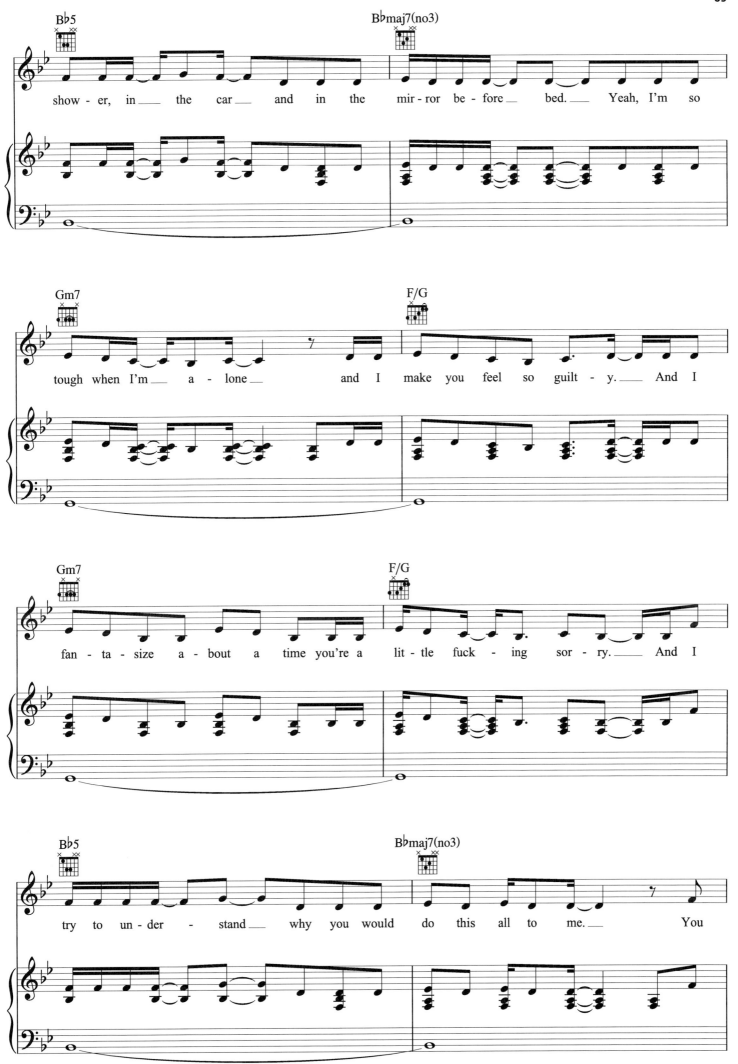

PRETTY ISN'T PRETTY

Words and Music by OLIVIA RODRIGO,
DANIEL NIGRO and AMY ALLEN

TEENAGE DREAM

Words and Music by OLIVIA RODRIGO
and DANIEL NIGRO

Visit Hal Leonard Online at **www.halleonard.com**

Explore the entire family of Hal Leonard products and resources